MARY HOOPER

The Never-ending Birthday

Illustrated by Harmen van Straaten

MACDONALD YOUNG BOOKS

Text copyright © Mary Hooper 1999
Illustrations copyright © Harmen van Straaten 1999

First published in Great Britain in 1999
by Macdonald Young Books
an imprint of Wayland Publishers Ltd
61 Western Road, Hove
East Sussex BN3 1JD

Find Macdonald Young Books on the internet at
http://www.myb.co.uk

The right of Mary Hooper to be identified as the author
of this Work and the right of Harmen van Straaten to be
identified as the illustrator of this Work has been asserted
by them in accordance with the Copyright, Designs and
Patents Act 1988.

Designed and Typeset by Don Martin
Printed in Hong Kong
British Library Cataloguing in Publication Data available

ISBN: 0 7500 2856 4

Chapter One

It was Saturday. It was also Jamie's most favourite day of the year – his birthday! Jamie sat up in bed and looked around him. He was *really* pleased with what he saw.

At the foot of Jamie's bed there was a big shiny red balloon. There was a silver banner across the doorway saying HAPPY BIRTHDAY TO YOU! and beside his bed was a large pile of brightly coloured parcels.

It was all *very* exciting.

"Morning, Jamie!" his mum said, coming in with his breakfast on a tray. "Happy Birthday!"

"Thanks, Mum," Jamie said, and he looked to see if there were any extra presents on the tray. There weren't, but there were some cards. Jamie opened the cards and took the money out. Then he was ready for his breakfast.

"It's your favourite!" Mum said. "Sausages and chips, with lots of ketchup. And chocolate milkshake after."

After breakfast, during which a lot of ketchup and chocolate milkshake were spilled on the duvet cover, Jamie opened all of his presents.

This is what Jamie got:
   A toy garage
   Six toy cars
   A fishing rod
   A computer game
   A *Zak the Space Invader* starship
   A big safari board game with
      blow-up animals

Jamie played with his presents for at least five minutes. Then he went downstairs to see what other exciting things were going to happen on his birthday.

All morning, Jamie was spoilt rotten. He watched videos, ate chocolates until he felt sick, and didn't get dressed until lunchtime.

Chapter Two

In the afternoon, Jamie's aunties
arrived and made a great fuss of him.

They brought more presents.

And more cards.

And balloons and posters and
badges.

Jamie loved being the centre of attention. While the aunties watched, he gave a brilliant performance on his recorder, then sang 'Happy Birthday to Me!' whilst juggling three balls in the air.

"Aren't you marvellous!" all the aunties said.

"Such talent!"

"You should be on TV!"

At three o'clock, Jamie was going to have a big party. Everyone in his class was invited. There was going to be a yummy tea, a magician with real rabbits and large goodie bags for everybody.

The aunties helped Jamie's mum
prepare an enormous amount of food.
There were mountains of sandwiches,
extra-wobbly jellies, huge sausage
rolls, nice fat cream buns, iced biscuits
with 'J' on them and chocolate sauce
on all the puddings.

At the stroke of three, the guests started arriving. Everyone who came brought a present (Jamie made sure of this before he let them in).

He tore the wrappings off his presents and put them in piles. "Decent", "average", "pooey", he muttered to himself as he sorted them out. He didn't bother much with the cards (unless they were gift vouchers).

All the children played some games (which Jamie won) and then it was time for tea.

The table was so full of food, it was a wonder its legs could still hold it up. Everyone ate as much food as they possibly could.

"I can't wait for the magician!" Ben said as he licked his fingers.

"He's got real white rabbits!" said Meera. "I *love* rabbits."

After tea, Mum brought in the birthday cake. It was so big, Jamie had to stand on a chair to see over it.

"If you blow out all the candles you can have a wish!" said Mum, and the aunties stood by, with their cameras at the ready.

Jamie blew out every candle with one puff and the aunties' cameras flashed.

"What do you wish for?" everyone cried.

Jamie looked around greedily at the presents and cards and balloons. "I wish that every day was my birthday!" he said.

There was a huge flash and then...

Chapter Three

It was Saturday. It was also Jamie's
most favourite day of the year – his
birthday. Jamie sat up in bed and
looked around him. He was pleased
with what he saw.

"Morning, Jamie," Mum said, bringing in his breakfast. "Happy birthday again, son!"

"Thanks," Jamie said, and he picked out the cards which had money in and left the rest. Then he looked at his breakfast.

"Where are my sausages?" he asked.

"I didn't have time to go shopping," said Mum. She eyed the presents by the side of the bed. "Hmm," she said. "I don't know where we're going to put all this stuff."

By eleven o'clock, Jamie was rather sick of chocolates. And he'd seen all the videos the day before.

In the afternoon Jamie's aunties arrived.

"Watch me! I'm going to juggle and sing 'For I'm a Jolly Good Fellow!' " Jamie said. And he did. For quite a long time.

The aunties watched him and said, "Very nice," and "That's interesting, dear," and "Mmm..."

At three o'clock the guests started
arriving. Jamie opened two of the
presents but after that he didn't
bother.

"Put it on that pile over there,"
he told each of his guests.

"No! Not the 'decent' pile," he shouted at Meera. "Yours goes on the 'pooey' pile."

Meera stared at Jamie. She wanted to say something rude back to him, but it was his birthday.

They played the same games as the day before. Jamie won again.

"D'you think we'll get to see the magician today?" Ben asked Meera.

"D'you think we'll get to see the rabbits?" Meera asked Ben. Then she sighed and said, "No, I don't think so."

On the party food front, Jamie's mum had run out of posh sandwich fillings, so there wasn't quite as much food as the day before.

After tea, Mum brought in the birthday cake.

"If you blow out all the candles
you can have a wish!" she said, and
all the children looked at each other
nervously.

Jamie blew out every candle with
one puff. And then he looked round
at the presents and cards and posters
and balloons.

"Oh, no!" Meera muttered.

"Not again!" groaned Ben.

Jamie smiled greedily. "I wish that every day was my birthday!"

There was a huge flash and then...

It was Saturday. It was also Jamie's most favourite day of the year – his birthday...

Chapter Four

After five of Jamie's birthdays,
everyone was heartily sick of them.
They were a bit fed up with Jamie, too.

Jamie stomped out of bed and went
to the door. "Mum!" he yelled. "Where's
my special birthday breakfast?"

Jamie's mum came to the foot of the stairs. "If you want something to eat you'll have to make it yourself!" she shouted up.

"But it's my birthday!" Jamie complained.

"It's always your birthday these days," Mum said grumpily. "That's just the trouble."

Downstairs, birthday cards littered the house and the floor was covered with wrapping paper. Jamie opened a box of chocolates but took one look and put the lid back quickly.

His mum came in with the vacuum cleaner. "Jamie," she said, "if you're going to carry on having these birthdays you've got to do a bit more round the house."

Jamie sighed, but he helped his mum to tidy up. He was rather thoughtful as he did so.

Then, he had to help prepare the party food. Jamie hated doing this, but luckily, the sandwiches were quite easy because there was only bread and butter left.

In the afternoon the aunties arrived.
They rushed past Jamie, put their
presents in the corner and put the
TV on.

Jamie coughed loudly. "I'm going to entertain you by standing on my head and singing 'God Save the Queen' backwards!" he announced.

But the aunties hardly noticed.

Jamie looked at them, frowned, and became even more thoughtful.

At three o'clock the party guests
started arriving. Jamie took their
presents and tossed them over his
head into a pile.

They started to play the same games as before. After a moment Meera said, "Shall we not bother?"

Ben shook his head. "There's no point," he said. "We might as well give you the prizes straight away, Jamie. You're going to win anyway."

"Oh... er... yes," Jamie said.
"I suppose we might as well." And he
frowned.

When Jamie's mum brought in the
party food, no one had much of an
appetite. Especially when they saw
what was on offer.

While everyone was looking outside, Meera quickly took one of the candles off the cake. Then she put on a very special candle of her own.

Jamie's mum rapped the table. "Oh, do come on, Jamie," she said. "If you blow out all the candles you can have a wish."

All the children looked at each other.

Jamie puffed. And he puffed.

And he puffed.

Jamie blew out every other candle. But whatever he did, he couldn't blow out Meera's special candle.

After a moment everyone started smiling.

"Oh dear, you don't get a wish!"
Mum said cheerfully.

"Oh, what a shame!" all the
children cried.

"Oh, thank heavens for that," said
the aunties.

Then they all cheered, Jamie's mum cut huge slices of birthday cake for everyone and the aunties hugged each other. Even Jamie breathed a sigh of relief. He realized he wasn't very nice when he had too many birthdays.

And Meera got to see the rabbits at last, because then the magician arrived and started doing tricks...

Look out for more exciting new titles in the Shooting Stars series:

My Dad Is... by Ali Ives

When Becky Harris has to write an essay about her dad, she has a huge problem. She doesn't have a dad! So she decides to make one up. First she pretends that he's a doctor, then a chef, then a photocopier salesman, then an actor, but none of her dads seem to be quite right. What is she going to do?

Cinderella's Wedding by Paeony Lewis

Cinderella loves the Prince and the Prince loves her. Planning a wedding should be easy... but not if Cinderella's ugly sisters Hiccup and Nosy have anything to do with it. They both think they will be the one to say 'I do'. Will the Prince ever end up marrying the woman of his dreams?

You can buy all these books from your local bookseller, or they can be ordered direct from the publisher. For more information about the Shooting Stars series, write to: The Sales Department, Macdonald Young Books, 61 Western Road, Hove, East Sussex BN3 1JD